• MY BOOK OF •
Numbers, Colours, Shapes and Sizes

Introduction

This book is intended for parents and children to share together. Here are some suggestions to help you both get the most from this book:

- When reading, always allow plenty of time for your child to look at and talk about the pictures.

- Read the rhymes to your child and ask the child to answer the questions. Don't hesitate to offer help in answering the questions by pointing out clues in the rhyme which correspond to the picture.

- Try to find examples of numbers, colours, shapes and sizes at home and when you and your child are out together.

- Always give plenty of encouragement and praise.

Numbers, Colours, Shapes and *Sizes* first published 1989
by The Parent and Child Programme,
an imprint of Reed International Books
Sizes first published as *Big and Small*

This edition published 1992 by Dean,
Michelin House, 81 Fulham Road, London SW3 6RB

Numbers illustrated by Dom Mansell
Colours illustrated by Andy Cooke
Shapes illustrated by Tony Wells
Sizes illustrated by Louise Voce

© Reed International Books 1992

ISBN 0 603 55043 6

Produced by Mandarin
Printed in Hong Kong

• MY BOOK OF •
Numbers, Colours, Shapes and Sizes

Written and designed by
David Bennett

DEAN

Numbers

Tips for reading together

Help your child to count the animals in the pictures.
Point out the details mentioned in the text, for
example, the three eggs belonging to the three birds.

Counting each object involves much more than being able
to recite the numbers in order. It is a skill which
needs time to develop.

On further readings, see if your child can find other
examples of the number on each page, five butterflies
on page five, for example.

0

This is the cage where
I sang each day.
The door was left open
So I flew away.

Who am I?

There is **1** of me.

I've got one trunk,
It's so full of power,
It sucks up the water
And gives me a shower.

Who am I?

There are **2** of us.

We each have two eyes
That are big, black and round.
We play in the trees,
High up from the ground.

Who are we?

There are **3** of us.

We each have a nest,
With three little eggs
And when we sit down,
You can't see our legs.

Who are we?

There are **4** of us.

We each have four legs
That go clippety-clop.
We can run, we can jump,
But we really can't hop.

Who are we?

There are **5** of us.

On each of our feet,
We have five wriggly toes.
We are covered in fur —
We don't need to wear clothes!

Who are we?

There are **6** of us.

We have six little legs
To cling to the flowers.
We go buzz, buzz, buzz,
In the garden for hours.

Who are we?

There are **7** of us.

On our pretty red wings
There are seven black spots.
We crawl around plants,
And hide in flower pots.

Who are we?

There are **8** of us.

We have eight spindly legs
For scuttling around.
People scream when they see us —
We don't make a sound.

Who are we?

There are **9** of us.

We have nine babies each,
All hopping around.
We play in the fields,
But sleep underground.

Who are we?

Colours

Tips for reading together

Ask your child to look carefully at the picture and choose the animal of the correct colour. A stroke of the correct colour appears alongside the rhyme to help the child.

Talk about the colour of the animal in the rhyme and see if your child can point out other examples of the same colour in the picture.

I like black, black is best.

Black is dark,
Like the night.
Black goes really
Well with white.

Who am I?

I like red, red is best.

Red is bright,
Rich and loud.
Red stands out
From the crowd.

Who am I?

I like yellow, yellow is best.

Yellow is light,
Like the sun.
Yellow makes me
The pretty one.

Who am I?

I like blue, blue is best.

Blue is cold,
Like the sea.
Blue is great,
Just like me.

Who am I?

I like orange, orange is best.

Orange is warm,
Like a flame.
Orange is strong...
And I'm the same.

Who am I?

I like green, green is best.

Green is fresh,
Like leaves in spring.
On this green leaf
I croak and sing.

Who am I?

I like brown, brown is best.

Brown is muddy,
Like a puddle.
My fur is brown
And soft to cuddle.

Who am I?

I like pink, pink is best.

Pink is gentle,
Soft and pale.
Chicks like to swing
On my pink tail.

Who am I?

I like grey, grey is best.

Grey is dull,
Like a cloudy day.
But grey is lively
When I'm at play.

Who am I?

I like all colours,
All colours are best.
I'm the colours
Of all the rest.

Who am I?

Shapes

Tips for reading together

Talk about the shape – not only its name, but how many sides it has, whether they are straight or curved, etc.

See if your child can point out other examples of the same shape in the picture. Or, after several readings, see if your child can pick out different shapes in the same picture, for example, circles on the diamond page.

Point out examples of shapes in everyday objects – for example, circular clocks or wheels, oblong-shaped windows or food packets.

Circle

My wheels are circles
That go round and round.
They help me to race
On the bumpity ground.

What am I?

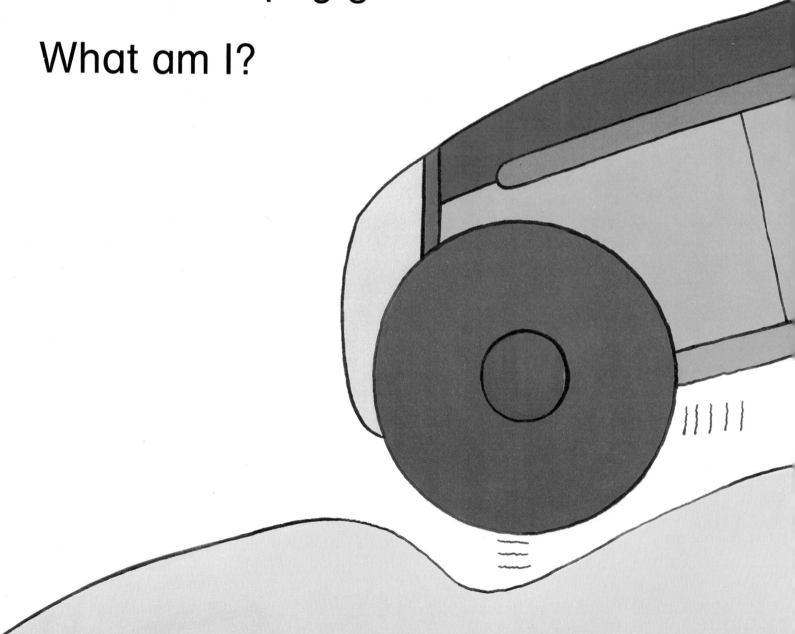

Square

I am a square,
You can use me to play.
Just throw the dice
And then you're away.

What am I?

Oblong

My bricks are oblongs
That build into walls.
My door is an oblong
Where the postman calls.

What am I?

Triangle △

My sail is a triangle,
With points one, two, three.
The wind blows me over
The deepest blue sea.

What am I?

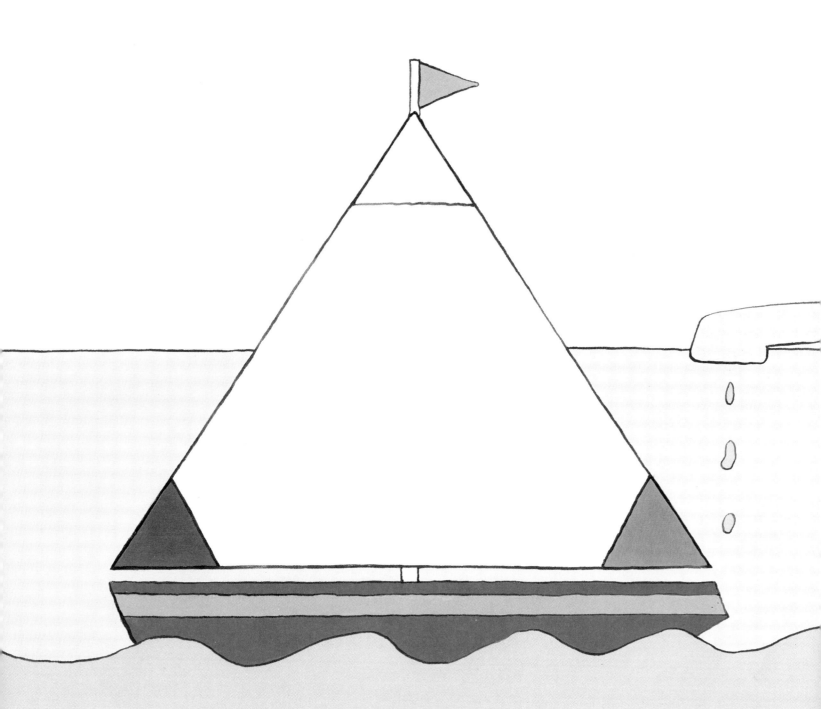

Diamond

I soar through the clouds,
High up in the sky.
My diamond shape
Helps me to fly.

What am I?

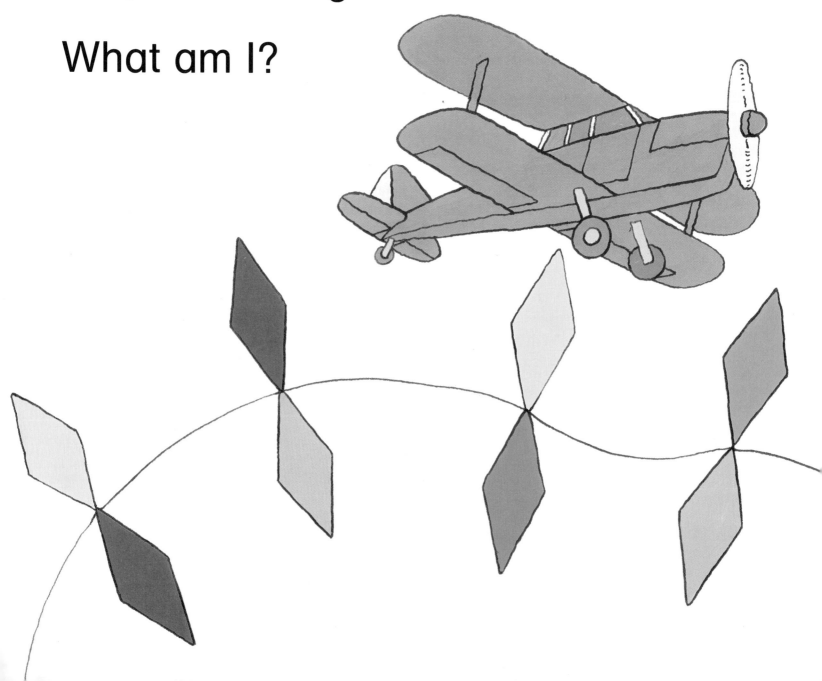

Star

I can sit on the top
Of a Christmas tree.
Cut shapes in the sand
To look just like me.

What am I?

Zigzags

I have got zigzags
Right down my back.
I breathe out hot fire
And my tongue is all black.

What am I?

Egg shape

I am shaped like an egg,
But I'm not in a cup.
If you fill me with air,
I go up, up, up!

What am I?

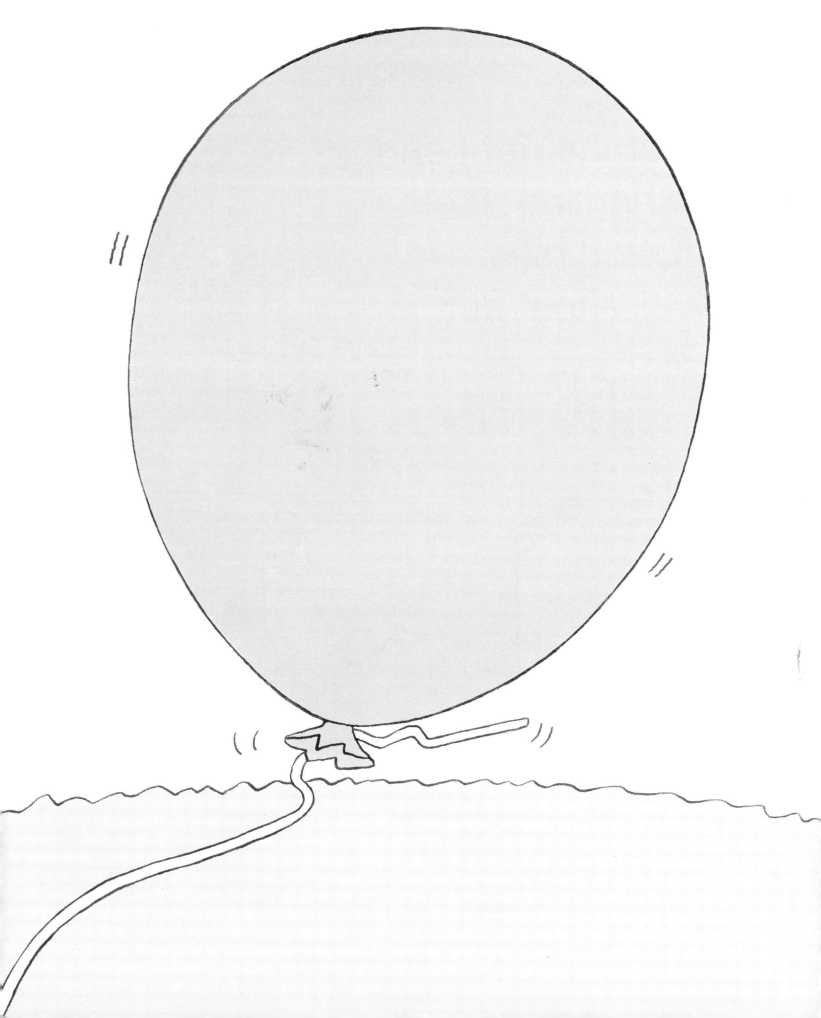

Wavy line

I'm just the right shape
For wriggling about.
I only say hisssss —
I never shout out.

What am I?

Now look at me,
I'm really the best.
I have the shapes
Of all of the rest.

What am I?

Sizes

Tips for reading together

Talk about the sizes of the animals in the pictures,
and use the last page to talk about the biggest,
smallest, etc.

Discuss the sizes of things in your home. You could
play a game where your child collects objects – each
one being bigger than the last!

I am teeny-tiny,
I creep and I crawl.
I'm sure that I am
The smallest of all.

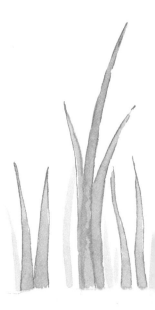

Who am I?

I am bigger than her,
But still rather small.
I can run very fast,
Although I'm not tall.

Who am I?

I am bigger than him,
But still small and sweet.
I go quack, quack, quack
And not tweet, tweet, tweet.

Who am I?

I am bigger than her,
I can leap, jump and run
And chasing young birds
Is my best kind of fun.

Who am I?

I am bigger than him,
I bark and I play.
With one look at me,
The cat runs away.

Who am I?

I am bigger than her
And I eat, eat, eat.
I am fat, pink and round,
With stubby little feet.

Who am I?

I am bigger than him,
I grunt and I growl.
You had better watch out
When I'm on the prowl.

Who am I?

I am bigger than her,
So just listen to me.
I splash in the mud,
Till I'm ready for tea.

Who am I?

I am bigger than him,
Much bigger by far.
My ears and long nose
Make me the star.

Who am I?

Who is big
And who is small?
Who is the biggest
Of us all?